For Miss Pacula, my second-year art teacher at Dame Alice Owen's

DRAW WITH ROB

HarperCollins*Children'sBooks*

First published in paperback in Great Britain by
HarperCollins *Children's Books* in 2021

HarperCollins *Children's Books* is a division of HarperCollins*Publishers* Ltd.
Text and illustrations copyright © Rob Biddulph 2021
The author/illustrator asserts the moral right to
be identified as the author/illustrator of the work.
A CIP catalogue record for this book is available from
the British Library. All rights reserved.

HarperCollins *Publishers* Ltd, 1 London Bridge Street, London SE1 9GF
HarperCollins*Publishers*, 1st Floor, Watermarque Building,
Ringsend Road, Dublin 4, Ireland

Visit our website at www.harpercollins.co.uk

1 3 5 7 9 8 6 4 2

ISBN: 978-0-00-841913-4

Printed and bound in the UK by
Bell & Bain Ltd.

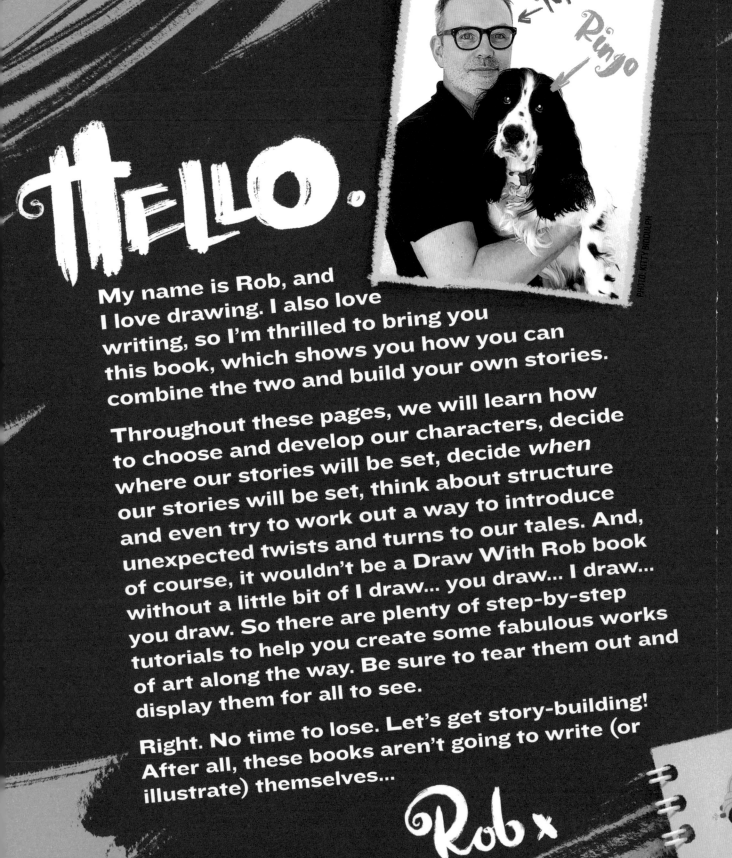

←Me

Ringo

PHOTO: KITTY BIDDULPH

HELLO.

My name is Rob, and I love drawing. I also love writing, so I'm thrilled to bring you this book, which shows you how you can combine the two and build your own stories.

Throughout these pages, we will learn how to choose and develop our characters, decide where our stories will be set, decide *when* our stories will be set, think about structure and even try to work out a way to introduce unexpected twists and turns to our tales. And, of course, it wouldn't be a Draw With Rob book without a little bit of I draw... you draw... I draw... you draw. So there are plenty of step-by-step tutorials to help you create some fabulous works of art along the way. Be sure to tear them out and display them for all to see.

Right. No time to lose. Let's get story-building! After all, these books aren't going to write (or illustrate) themselves...

Rob x

You will need...

A pencil...

Or a pen...

A pencil sharpener...

An eraser...

Something to colour with...

A notebook...

and a stapler.

Okay, let's get started!

BRICK by

Building a story is a lot like building a house – you need to put it all together, brick by brick. We need to figure out what those bricks are, so that we can see what your story will look like when you finish. On this page you'll find all of the basic building blocks you'll need, so let's get started on putting them all together...

WHO?

The first brick in your story is your main character (or characters). You need to decide who (or what) they are. What's really exciting is the fact that they can be anyone, or anything, you like! Let your creativity run wild.

WHERE?

The next thing to do is to decide where your story will happen. Is it somewhere real, maybe somewhere you've visited before, or is it an imaginary place?

WHEN?

Next, think about when you'd like your story to happen. It could be today, tomorrow, a long time ago or maybe at some point in the far-off future. It's entirely up to you.

WHAT?

Finally, you need to figure out what's going to happen in your story. It can be as exciting, as scary, as fun, as silly or as hilarious as you like. Whatever you decide, you have the power to make it happen.

BRICK

AND THE MOST IMPORTANT THING...

One thing is the **MOST** important of all when it comes to building a story. You already have it, and it's written right here on this page. The letters are all mixed up though, so can you unscramble them and figure it out?

Imaganation

WHO WHO WHOOOOOO?

The first thing we'll start with is **WHO** you want in your story. What do you want them to LOOK like on the outside, and what do you want them to BE like on the inside? Think about the books and movies you love, and which characters you like best. Remember, they don't have to be people, and they can be either good or bad. I've listed some of my favourites below, and shown you one of my characters on the page opposite (listing his characteristics) to help you get started.

Some of MY favourite characters

1 The Grinch

2 Hermione Granger

3 Han Solo

4 Paddington Bear

5 Scout Finch

6 Charlie Brown

Some of YOUR favourite characters

1

2

3

4

5

6

HEROES & VILLAINS

Lots of stories have a hero – the goodie – and a villain – the baddie. Most of the time, they're not all good or all bad, but a mixture of the two, just like in real life. Can you follow the strings here, and join the hero or villain up with their equipment?

FRED BEAR

VAMPYRA

SUPERHERO BEAR

BORIS BEAR

Meet BORIS

Boris is a bear who wants to win, and he'll even cheat to do it (by stealing Fred's **GRRRRR!**). But maybe Boris isn't as bad as he seems, and he's certainly still fun to draw! Turn the page to learn how...

How to Draw...

Boris

From the book *GRRRRR!*

1 First, draw two small rectangles at the top of the page, with a horizontal line above them. These are his glasses. Just add two dots for his eyes!

2 Next, draw a vertical rectangle down from the middle of the glasses and add a small, coloured-in oblong for his nose.

3 At each end of his glasses, draw a small semicircle on top. These are Boris's ears. Then draw a square shape below for his head.

4 Now for my favourite bit: let's give Boris a moustache! Draw a curved line under his nose with a small spiral on each end.

5 Draw a rectangle with curved corners just below his head. Then, head down and out on each side, adding a straight line to join them together across the bottom.

6 Underneath that, draw a curved line like you see here. Then give Boris legs by adding a rectangle on each side – with some claws at the bottom of each.

7 Arms next. Add a curved sausage shape with rounded ends on each side as shown, with a curved rectangle on each for a cuff. Then draw his claws on each hand.

8 It's colouring time! I've used dark colours and a stripy sweater to make him look mysterious, but you can use any colours you like. Add a scribbly shadow underneath him too.

By _____ Age _____

BORIS

How do you spot a superhero? By their costume, of course! Every good hero needs a SUPER outfit, and it's time to design one for yours. Take a look at the options below, and let's get drawing...

WE NEED a (super) HERO!

Masks

Capes

Boots and belts

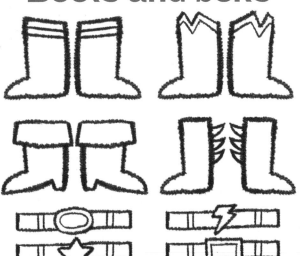

Suits

a superhero bear

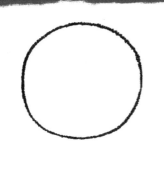

1 Draw a big circle in the top half of the page.

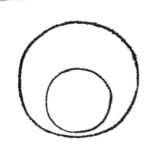

2 Next, add a smaller circle inside the big one, in the bottom half.

3 Add two circular shapes at the top, like you see here. These are your bear's ears.

4 Let's add some details. Draw a smaller circle inside each ear, as shown. Then give your bear two dots for eyes, and a very small circle for a nose. Then add a smile, and join it to the nose with a vertical line.

5 Give your bear a mask by drawing a horizontal line just above and just below the eyes. Then add two small, tilted lines above the eyes, for eyebrows.

6 Time for a body! Draw another circle underneath the head. Add four horizontal lines and an oval to join them together for a belt.

7 Add a bent sausage shape to each side for arms, like you see here, and two more sausage shapes for legs.

8 Your bear needs a cape. Draw a triangle behind everything, as I have done here. Some straight lines across the legs and arms create gloves and boots, and some tiny triangles on each glove will finish them off.

9 Finally, let your imagination soar and add some colour to your superhero bear! Don't forget to add the costume you designed, and some scribbly shadow under your hero.

SUPERhero BEAR

By... Age............

WHERE in the WORLD?

Now you need to decide **WHERE** you want your story to be. The possibilities are endless. It can be a real place, or somewhere from your imagination; it's entirely up to you. I've given you a few ideas here, but see if you can think of some more. Oh, and can you also complete the names of the countries on the flags?

GREENLAND

C

U K

F
8

S
7

5

1

U S of A

4

The Big City

13

W

A desert island

B

16

The Rainforest

PERU

18

A

The Seven Seas

Outer space

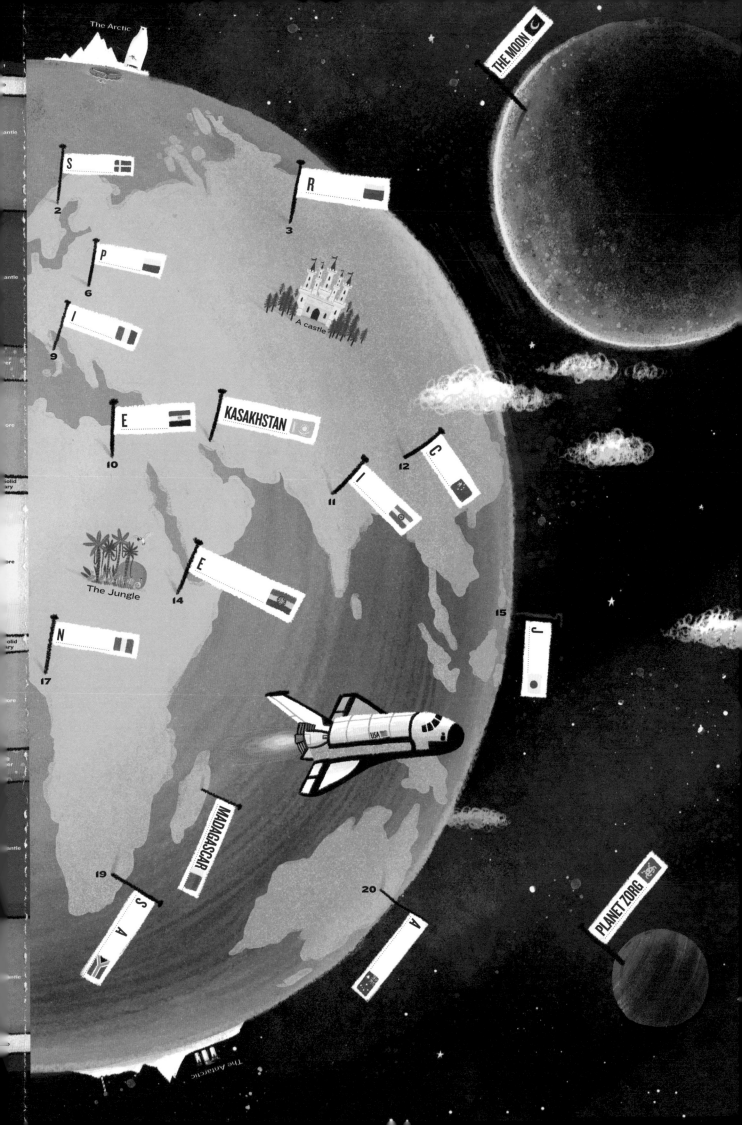

RAISE the DRAWBRIDGE

The **evil queen** is hiding from the dragon in her castle, which is filled with spooky corridors and exciting hidden rooms to explore. Draw what you think the inside of the castle should look like.

INTO the WOODS

The evil queen has kidnapped a unicorn and is holding it prisoner in the castle! Can you help the brave princess and her knight get through the enchanted forest and come to the rescue? Watch out for traps along the way!

Meet the UNICORN

The unicorn is a magical creature that rules over the enchanted forest, using its magic to bring happiness to the kingdom. Let's learn how to draw it, but keep an eye out for anyone wanting to steal its powers...

How to DRAW...
a unicorn

I Start by drawing an upside-down ice-cream cone shape at the top of the page.

2 Underneath that, add an oval shape with a jagged bottom, like you see here.

3 Next, draw a long, curved shape underneath. Towards the top of that shape, draw two circles with dots in the middle, for eyes. Then add eyelashes by drawing little lines all round the edge.

4 Draw a thin, curved line further down the nose, as shown. Add two small spirals below that for nostrils, and then a little curve at the bottom for a smile.

5 Add two oval shapes with pointy ends on either side of the unicorn's horn for ears, and a smaller, similar shape inside them. Voila! Your unicorn has a head!

6 Just below the unicorn's head, draw a circle on either side. Draw a smaller circle inside each one.

7 Draw two rectangles between the circles for front legs, with curved lines at the bottom to look like hooves. Add a little line on each side to join the big circles back to the head, as shown.

8 Your unicorn needs a mane! Create one by drawing a jagged line on either side of the head, like you see here.

9 For the final magical touch, add colour to your unicorn – any you like. Then add a scribbly shadow underneath,

UNICORN

By .... Age ....

an evil queen

1 Let's start with the queen's crown! Draw six points, joined up with a straight line along the bottom. Add jewels by putting a tiny circle on the top of each point.

2 Next, draw a heart underneath the crown.

3 Join the heart to the crown by drawing a big curved line out from each side. Inside the heart, give the queen a face, by copying what you see here. Notice how the eyebrows make her look evil!

4 Add a circle under her chin, then draw two big arrowhead shapes either side of it, joining them to her head.

5 Coming down from the points you've just drawn, sketch two rectangle shapes that get wider at the bottom, one on either side of the circle. These are her sleeves.

6 Next, draw a hand coming from the bottom of each sleeve, as you see here. Then add a long, thin rectangle behind them, with a small knob at one end and a bigger circle with a jagged line through it at the other.

7 Finally, draw a line curving out from the bottom of each sleeve, and join them up with a horizontal line. Add two more curved lines as shown. Your queen is dressed!

8 An evil queen needs some colour! Use your imagination and make her as bright or as dark as you like.

EViL QUEEN

By... Age..............

ONCE UPON A TIME...

WHEN your story happens is just as important as where it is, and who is in it. It can be set a long, long time ago, or it can take place just yesterday. It can happen tomorrow afternoon or far, far ahead in the distant future. Take a look at the timeline below, fill in some ideas in the spaces provided and let your imagination run wild...

WHEN DINOSAURS ROAMED THE EARTH

IDEA 1

WHEN PIRATES SAILED THE SEVEN SEAS

MILLIONS OF YEARS AGO

TIME

THE ICE AGE

WHEN A MEDIEVAL KING RULED THE LAND

IDEA 2

IDEA 3

THE WILD WEST

JUST
LAST
WEEK

THE 1970s

MILLIONS
OF YEARS
FROM NOW

LINE

THE
1930s

THE
1980s

THE
DISTANT
FUTURE

AGE of the DINOSAURS

A long, long time ago, dinosaurs ruled the Earth and terrified the cavemen and cavewomen. **Or did they?** Take a look at the picture and circle ten things that are wrong with it.

Welcome to Pangaea

FOUR SEASONS IN ONE Dog

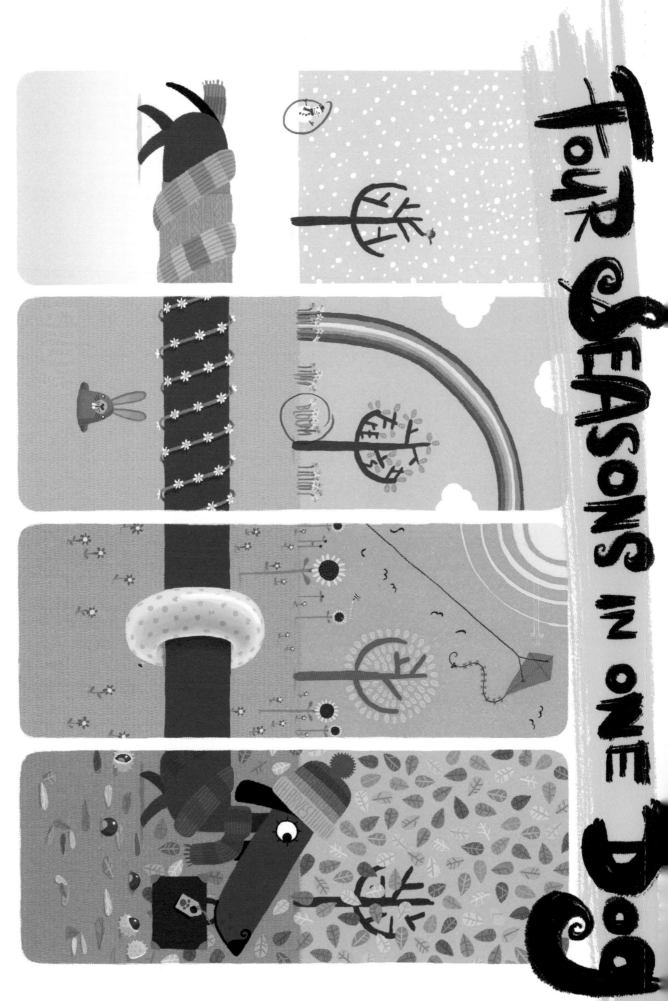

Stories happen all year round. There are twelve seasonal words hidden in this picture of the **Odd Dog Out**. Can you find them all?

IN a GALAXY FAR FROM HERE...

1
2
3
4
5

Zorg the Explorer has treasures from all the ages of Earth to take back to his cosmic museum for **Show and Tell**. Can you spot the five differences between the two pictures?

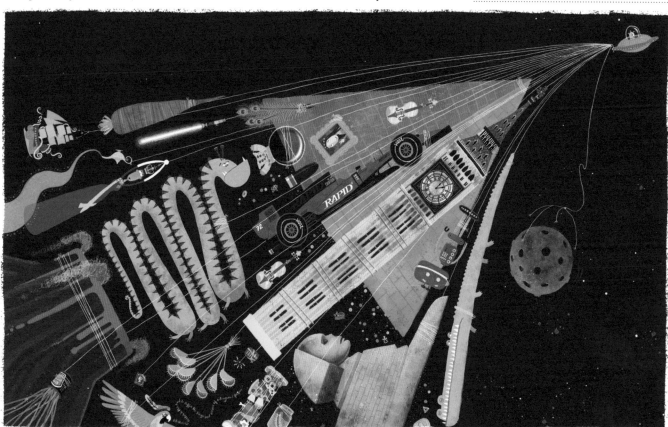

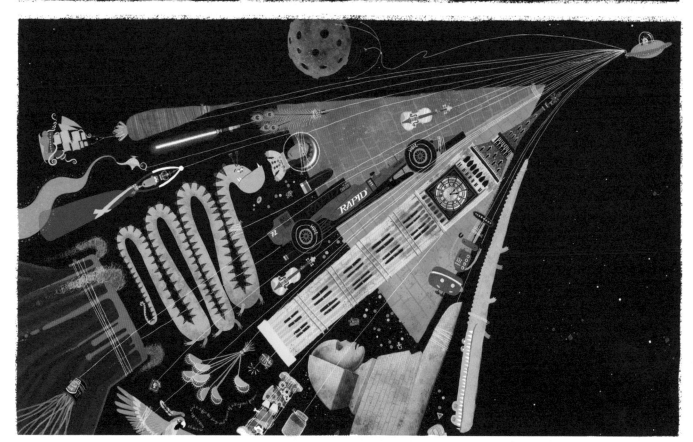

1 Let's start with something really easy. Draw a rectangle with curved corners at the top of the page, as shown.

2 Then add two circles inside it, one on either side.

3 Draw a vertical rectangle in the middle, and line the inside of it with small dots. Then draw a horizontal rectangle underneath that and fill it with a zigzagging line.

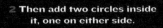

4 Below that, draw another rectangle for a body, and join it to the top one with two small lines to make your robot's neck.

5 Two curvy shapes, one on either side, will be your robot's arms. And two rectangles coming down from the body will be the legs!

6 Next, stack three rectangles on each side of your robot's head as shown. Draw an upside-down **U** shape at the end of each arm for robot hands, and a long, stretched-out oval at the bottom of the legs.

7 Inside that long oval, draw a line of small circles so your robot can roll along on its track. Add lots of little lines round the outside too, so it will have some grip.

8 Now, your robot needs some details! Give it some antennas on the top of its head, and as many buttons and dials on its body as you can fit, like I have drawn here.

9 Your robot isn't complete without colour. Use everything in your toolbox to make it as bright as you can, and don't forget to add a shadow underneath!

ROBOT

By... Age.............

AWAY TO THE MOON

In the not-too-distant future, Harry has flown to the moon and is trying to claim it as his own. But it looks like someone else got there first! Use your drawing skills to show who it is...

Planet
HARRY

It's STORYTIME

Now that you know who is going to be in your story, as well as where and when it will take place, the final step to building your story is to decide **WHAT** is going to happen! It might sound simple, but your story will need a **beginning**, a **middle** and an **end**. So let's get started. Remember, anything can happen!

In the beginning...

The start of your story is where we meet the characters and find out when and where the story is set. Take a look at the ideas below, and then come up with your own.

....

On a particularly quiet day in outer space, many years from now...

....

A long time ago, when pirates ruled the waves, a bottle washed up on an island...

....

The night was dark and stormy, and Princess Varinia should have been in bed...

....

....

....

....

....

....

....

....

In the middle...

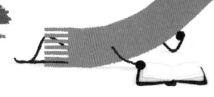

The middle of the story is where things happen! This is where you put all the exciting events you can think of. You can put as few or as many as you like; just keep it going. I'll get you started below.

....

The spaceman steps out of his rocket and sees a bright green alien. Then...

....

A penguin found a message in the bottle. It told the penguin to swim out into the sea and wait by the third wave from the left. So she did...

....

The brave princess explored the scary castle and met... a wailing ghost! But...

....

....

....

....

....

....

....

In the end...

The end of your story is the most important part. This is where any problems are solved, and we find out if everything is going to be okay. It can be happy, sad, funny or strange! See what you can come up with.

....

The spaceman takes the alien back to Earth, and they open a shop selling moon cheese.

....

The penguin met a pirate captain, joined his crew and they sailed the seven seas.

....

The princess found out that the ghost was wailing because it was scared of the dark! So she gave it a night-light and went back to bed.

....

....

....

....

....

....

TREASURE HUNT

Penguin Blue and his pirate pals are back home after another adventure, with new friends, new stories to tell and new treasure. However, some things have been lost along the way. Can you find them in this picture?

CAPTAIN PLANK'S PIRATE PLAYGROUND

TICKETS

NEPTUNE'S DREAD

15 things to find

1 A treasure chest ☐
2 Wilbur Seal ☐
3 A skull-and-crossbones T-shirt ☐
4 A trampolining penguin ☐
5 A mermaid ☐
6 Clive the polar bear ☐
7 Two seagulls ☐
8 Penguin Blue ☐
9 Chatting penguins ☐
10 Penguins Jeff and Flo ☐
11 A climbing wall ☐
12 A treasure map ☐
13 Captain Walker Plank ☐
14 An anchor ☐
15 A bottle of rum ☐

HOW to DRAW...

Captain Walker Plank

From the book *Sunk!*

1 First, draw an upside-down U, and join up the bottom with an upside-down V, curving the top, like you see here.

2 Add a curved line underneath. This is his bottom jaw. Add two small spirals for nostrils, and lines for whiskers on each side, as shown.

3 Next, draw a circle with a dot in it on the right side, just above the whiskers, for an eye. A small black square on the left will be his eyepatch. Let's strap it on with a thick black line on both sides.

4 Draw a big, curved line over the top of everything, and join it up underneath the whiskers, like you see here.

5 Let's give him some tusks. Draw two long, pointed shapes coming down from his mouth; one on each side.

6 Next, draw a long, curved U shape coming down from his head. Add a wobbly line between his tusks, and give him a nice feathery hat, as shown here.

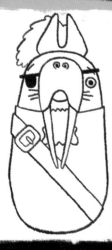

7 Two long, diagonal lines from the top left to the bottom right make a strap, and then add a buckle as shown. Draw some wobbly lines around the sides of his tusks too.

8 He still needs some flippers! Draw a rounded triangle coming out of either side of his body, with two lines across them to illustrate the cuffs, as shown.

9 Finally, add a shadow, some details and a spot of colour! I have given him gold buttons and braid, but what you draw is up to you.

![Draw with Rob logo]

Captain WALKER PLANK

By.. Age..........

How to DRAW...
a mermaid

1 Start by drawing a bowl shape in the top half of the page, with a point coming up from the left side.

2 Inside it, draw two circles with dots in the middle for eyes, and three little eyelash lines on each circle.

3 Draw a star shape above the point at the top, and use three curved lines to give your mermaid a smile and some eyebrows. I've given the little star a face too!

4 Add a long, curved shape with bumps along it behind the star shape, just like you see here.

5 Underneath all this, draw two shapes with bumpy tops, like I have here. Below that, add two teardrop shapes with pointed ends that join up in the middle.

6 She needs some arms! Under her head, draw two long shapes with bumps at the ends, one down from each side. Join it all together with some small lines as shown.

7 Draw a long arc over the top of it all. This is her hair. Join it up to her waist with a straighter line, as I have done here.

8 Give her a fishy tail! Draw some lines coming down from her waist and bending round to the left. Add two long leaf shapes at the end for the tail.

9 Finally, make your mermaid as bright and colourful as you like. The only limit is your imagination.

MERMAID

By.. **Age**

TURN iT UPSIDE DOWN

Some of the best stories don't end the way you think they will. Sometimes the hero isn't who you thought they were, and the bad guys aren't as bad as they seemed. Don't be afraid to **flip the script**! Add some colour to this unexpected story, and help the brave princess defeat the dragon.

HOW to DRAW... a dragon

1 Starting in the middle of the page, draw a line to the left. Then add two bumps. Then swoop down and back to the right, until you end up directly underneath where you started.

2 From the beginning of the first line, head up and over to the right, curving around as shown. Then head down the page, and swoop out to the right. Add a little hook at the end.

3 Finish the outline off as you see here; by joining it all up with a curved line with a long U shape sticking out from the bottom.

4 It's face time! Draw two dots in the bumps on the left, two circles with dots inside them for eyes, and a mouth full of sharp zigzag teeth.

5 Add two leafy shapes to the head for ears, as shown. Draw smaller leafy shapes inside them.

6 Draw two triangles between the ears for horns, and a U shape next to the tail for an arm. Then add another U shaped leg and lots of claws!

7 Draw a semicircle on your dragon's tummy and fill it with horizontal lines.

8 Let's add the final touches. Give your dragon blunt spikes all down his back and tail, and a wing halfway down. Just as I have done here.

9 Finally, it's time to colour! Your dragon can be as bright or as scary as you like, and don't forget the shadow underneath his feet. Oh, and the smoke coming out of his nose too!

DRAGON

By.. Age...........

How to Draw... a knight

1 Let's start with a shield. On the left side of your page, draw a curved V shape joined with a straight line at the top, like you see here. Draw the same shape inside it again.

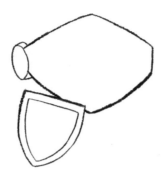

2 Just above that, draw a diamond on its side, but with the ends cut off. Use a straight line on the right and a circle on the left, just above the shield, as shown.

3 Fill that diamond shape with lots of long sausages, and add some dotty detail as shown here.

4 Draw a small bump on top of his head, and then add a big, bumpy, feathery shape to it, as shown. Easy!

5 Let's finish the bottom of his helmet. Add three lines under the circle on the left, and a long line with two smaller ones on the right, just like you see above.

6 Draw a square shape beneath the helmet, with two long, curvy points along the bottom where his waist will be. Add his arm and hand, as I have here. Fingers too!

7 Your knight's legs are two long rectangles coming down from his body, with points at the end and a circle in the middle.

8 Add some flat triangles for his feet, and fill them with lots of vertical lines to give the armour detail.

9 Make your new knight shiny and bright by adding colour, and a design on his shield. And don't forget the shadow under his feet!

By.. Age...........

KNIGHT

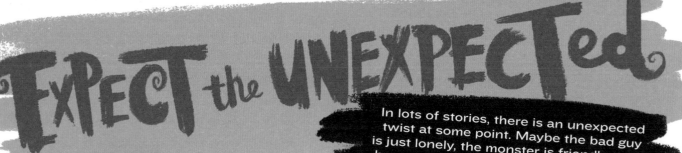

EXPECT the UNEXPECTed

In lots of stories, there is an unexpected twist at some point. Maybe the bad guy is just lonely, the monster is friendly or the hero was scared of something silly! See if you can think of a way to surprise people with your story.

Boris

A bad bear... or is he?

Cheated to win the Best Bear in the Wood contest

Just wants to make friends

Is really nice and cuddly

Big Foot

Terrifying monster

Big and scary

Loves reading

Knits his own scarves

Your character's name

The Terrible Troll

Teddy the pug is terrified of the terrible troll that lives in the scary shed – but what is he really afraid of? Join the dots and find out!

LAWN EATER 3000

How to Draw... a friendly monster

1 Nice and easy to start! Draw two circles touching in the middle, and put a big dot inside each one.

2 Underneath that, draw a bowl shape like you see here, with a smaller bowl shape just inside it

3 Give your monster a big, spiky smile by drawing a zigzag inside the smaller bowl shape.

4 Then draw two tilted lines for eyebrows, like I have here.

5 Your monster's body is a long, oval shape that surrounds everything that you've drawn so far. Make the top and the bottom of your oval shaggy, to show how furry he is.

6 Next, draw two bent, pointy shapes, one on each side of his head. These are his horns.

7 Draw a long, shaggy sausage shape on each side for his arms. They should hang below his body, as you can see here.

8 Add two shaggy rectangles underneath his body for his legs. You're almost done!

9 Every monster needs some colour! I've made mine stripy, but you can go as wild as you like with colours and patterns. Add a shadow underneath for the final touch.

MONSTER

By.. Age...........

BOOK IT!

Congratulations! You've built your story! Now it's time to turn it into a book, and draw the pictures to go with it. Let's start by deciding what you want on the cover.

The front cover

Try to give your reader an idea of what is inside through both the title and the picture on the front.

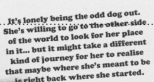

It's lonely being the odd dog out. She's willing to go to the other side of the world to look for her place in it... but it might take a different kind of journey for her to realise that maybe where she's meant to be is right back where she started.

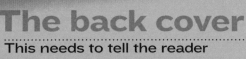

Meet Otto, Winnie, Greg(osaurus) and all the other dinosaur juniors, as they traverse life's first ups and downs.

Every dog has his Dave (or otherwise-named human)... but on a walk in the park, the adorable Teddy the pug loses his!

And when Teddy finds himself at the shed of the TERRIBLE TROLL in the woods, he might find more than he bargained for... a new friend.

The back cover

This needs to tell the reader what your story is about to get people interested in reading it! Keep it simple.

WHAT WILL YOURS LOOK LIKE?

Now, tear out the next three double-sided pages, and make your book.

By

Front cover

Fold along this line

DRAW WITH ROB

This is my book

AND IT'S TOTALLY ACE!

Back cover

3

6

4

5

PUT IT TOGETHER

Tear out the three double-sided pages before this one. Lie them down on top of each other in the following order:

• The page with the front and back covers goes on the bottom, with the front cover on the left, facing down.

• Put the page with numbers 2 and 7 on top of it, so you can see 2 and 7 the right way up.

• On top of that, put the page with numbers 4 and 5, so they are the right way up too.

Now, fold the pages along the dotted lines, and slot them together to form a book.

Staple them together.
(Staple them along the fold. You may need a grown-up to help you)

That's it! You've built your story, and now you've built an actual book too! Time to put it all together. Draw and write your front and back covers, and fill the inside pages with your story...

Finally, turn this page, because the gang and I have something to say...

CONGRATULATIONS ON YOUR FIRST BOOK

from ROB & the Gang

FOR MY NEXT TRICK...

You've built one story, but your imagination is limitless! Write down your ideas for more books here...

My next book

The one after that

The one after that

GOODBYE!

You've reached the end of this book. Well done, you!
I hope you've had fun drawing pictures and building a story with me,
and I hope that you keep creating more of your own.
You can read more of my stories in the books you see here.

 And don't forget to watch all of my
#DrawWithRob videos on my YouTube
channel and follow me on social media

@RobBiddulph @rbiddulph RobBiddulphAuthor Rob Biddulph @RobBiddulph

www.robbiddulph.com

ANSWERS

BRICK BY BRICK

The most important thing is... IMAGINATION!

HEROES & VILLAINS

WHERE IN THE WORLD?

1. Canada
2. Sweden
3. Russia
4. United States of America
5. United Kingdom
6. Poland
7. Spain
8. France
9. Italy
10. Egypt
11. India
12. China
13. Mexico
14. Ethiopia
15. Japan
16. Brazil
17. Nigeria
18. Argentina
19. South Africa
20. Australia

INTO THE WOODS

AGE OF THE DINOSAURS

Dinosaurs and people didn't live at the same time!

FOUR SEASONS IN ONE DOG

IN A GALAXY FAR FROM HERE

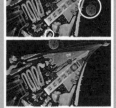

TREASURE HUNT

THE TERRIBLE TROLL